C000235048

A RHYMING ALPHABET OF MEDICINAL PLANTS

From the Garden
of the
Royal College of Physicians

© Henry Oakeley
2016

First published in Great Britain in 2016 by the author

Copyright © Henry Oakeley 2016

The moral right of the author has been asserted
ISBN 978-0-9521461-5-5
www.oakeleybooks.com

Introduction
A Rhyming Alphabet of Medicinal Plants

An alphabet book perhaps
Gives enjoyment to chaps
And to ladies and girls
With poetical whirls
But these whimsical rants
About the strange world of plants
Have a purpose more serious I claim
For they tell how they cure and they maim
And some more robust
Engender raw lust
And others I think
Are used to make drink
But don't be o'er awed
By many old frauds
Which will not cure sneezes
But induce diseases
And others 'tis plain
Are good for the brain
Or protect the growing foetus
From gestational diabetes

And beware the effects
Of plant cigarettes
And learn of the books
Once written by Fuchs
And others published solely
By the great Matthioli
And discover the status
Of *Acorus* in flatus
And uncontrolled trials
Of Figwort on piles
(We left that one out
As the book was too stout)
And more and yet more
Of knowledge of yore
All wondrously illustrated
With woodcuts antiquated
From various different herbals
To accompany the verbals
Which I hope you will enjoy ...

is for *Aconitum*
Of which Pliny said:
If swallowed in error
One ended up dead

Aconitum napellus, Wolf's bane, is so poisonous that Theophrastus (circa 340BC) reported that death was the punishment for possessing it.

Dioscorides (70AD) wrote that the seed heads and roots were placed on raw meat for killing wolves.

His contemporary, Pliny Secondus, added 'there is no poison in the world so quick in operation'.

is for *Acorus*
Which treats every ache
And stops a child's flatus
Should you compliments make

Acorus gramineus is the Japanese sweet flag. It is used throughout Asia for all sorts of aches and pains, as a tonic, for memory loss, insanity and more.

It is used to protect young children from a folk belief called 'Usog', a condition in which they suffer with wind if someone compliments them on their appearance.

 is for *Borage*
Which we put in our Pimms
But it contains more odd toxins
Than one can find in your MIMS

Borago officinalis, Borage, was held in high esteem by Nicholas Culpeper for its exhilarating qualities and for driving away sadness and melancholy, until it became suspected of causing damage to the liver, genetic abnormalities and cancer.

It was added to summer alcoholic drinks, but the UK Medicines Care Agency, now advises against this.

MIMS is the monthly pharmacopoeia received by UK physicians.

is for *Cynara*
The super cardoon,
It's in flower at the moment
But will be eaten quite soon

Cynara cardunculus, the Cardoon. The flower heads are eaten.

Dodoens (1552) thought them a cure for stinking armpits and that they engendered lust. Presumably in that order.

Galen (ca. 200AD) said they were indigestible unless cooked. However, he relates that other authors recommend the flower heads soaked in strong wine, to 'stir up lust in the body'.

is for *Capsicum*
I like it a lot;
Its colour is scarlet
Because it's so hot

Capsicum annuum, Chilli pepper, has been in cultivation in Latin America since 7,200BC, brought to Europe by the returning Columbus in the late 15th century. The chemical responsible for the hotness is capsaicin.

Various cultivars are used in cooking, and the strength (i.e. how hot they are) is measured in Scoville units.

A standard chilli pepper used in England would be around 5,000 Scovilles, the hottest peppers are rated over one million Scoville units.

atura is very interesting
It contains scopolamine
And soldiers who ingested it
Created quite a scene

Datura stramonium in Solanaceae is called Jimson Weed. It contains high concentrations of the neurotoxic alkaloid, scopolamine.

It gained its name from the town of Jamestown, Virginia, where, in 1676, some soldiers sent to put down the 'Bacon Rebellion' against Governor Berkeley were given plants as a boiled vegetable and hallucinated, even running around naked, for 11 days.

When they recovered they had no memory of the event – and probably no rifles or trousers if the rebels had seized the opportunity.

 is for *Equisetum*
Which is really very tragic
For taking it as cups of tea
Causes cystitis haemorrhagic

Equisetum hyemale, Mares' Tail.
Dioscorides and Pliny (1st century AD)
used it for coughs and pleurisy.

It is used to treat urinary tract infections,
drunk as a tea, but painful haemorrhagic
cystitis has been attributed to it.

The English *E. palustre* contains the
enzyme thiaminase, which breaks down
vitamin B1 in the body, causing death
from beri-beri of horses which eat it.

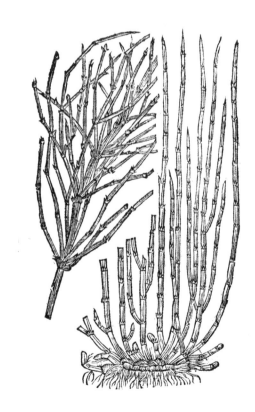

is for *Fuchsia*
And if I am not mistook
It celebrates dear Leonhart Fuchs
Who wrote a famous book

Fuchsia honours Leonhart Fuchs (1501-1566), author of *De Historia Stirpium commentarii insignes* (1542) and *Medendi Methodo* (1539), Professor of Medicine in Ingolstadt and founder of the botanic garden in Tübingen.

His *De Historia* is one of the world's great herbals, with over 500 life-like woodcuts of plants, set out in alphabetical order, with text mostly following the work of Dioscorides (70AD).

is for *Galanthus*
It contains galanthamine
You can take it for your memory
But it is a waste of time

Galanthus nivalis, the 'English' snowdrop contains galanthamine, which increases brain acetylcholine levels.

Used for treating Alzheimer's disease (in which decreased brain levels are found).

It does not arrest the progress of the disease, caused by the death of cells in the brain.

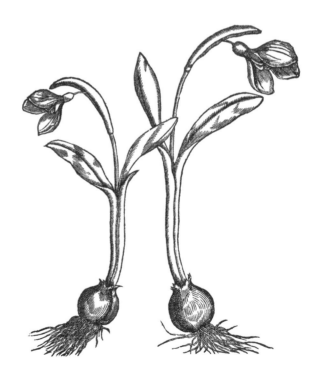

is for *Galega*
Greek for Goat's Rue
Diabetics get Metformin
From its flowers so blue

Guanidine and Galegine, chemicals present in *Galega officinalis*, Goat's Rue, treated diabetes, but were too toxic for use.

Related biguanides, particularly Metformin, were found to be safe and effective and it is now the commonest medicine used for diabetes worldwide.

It stops the liver releasing sugars, and increases the rate that sugars leave the blood and enter cells.

is for *Helianthus*
A sunny sort of flower
Whose seeds make a special oil
Your cholesterol to lower

Helianthus annuus, Sunflower.
Sunflower seed oil is used to make a
vegetable margarine.

Johnson (1633) wrote that 'the floure
of the Sun, Marigold of Peru: the buds
before they be floured [i.e. before they
come into flower], boiled and eaten with
butter, vinegar and pepper, after the
manner of Artichokes, are exceedingly
pleasant meat, surpassing the Artichoke
far in procuring bodily lust'.

is for *Hyoscyamus*
Which makes your pupils wide
But if you take a little more
Your mind and brains are fried

Hyoscyamus niger, black henbane: small amounts are medicinal, more is poisonous, causing a dry mouth, dilated pupils, a fast pulse, and an inability to sweat.

Turner (1551) recommended smoking the leaves for a cough, but from the time of Dioscorides (70AD) its use was known to cause 'madness' with hallucinations.

In small doses the chemicals in it are used as a pre-med before an operation and to treat sea sickness.

is for *Iris*
Which is very good for us
For it lowers serum glucose
In type 2 diabetes

Iris unguicularis, Algerian iris, has scientifically-based potential for treating diabetes.

The rhizomes contain the chemical kaempferol which reduces the rate of glucose absorption from the stomach.

This could be used to prevent the dangerous peaks of blood sugar that occur in diabetics and so reduce eye and kidney complications.

The unprocessed rhizome is toxic, causing 'nausea, vomiting, diarrhoea and skin irritation'.

is for Juniper
It's used to flavour gin
An aid to disinhibition
And facilitating sin

The name 'gin' comes from the Dutch word for juniper, jenever, a traditional alcoholic drink of the Netherlands and Belgium.

It became popular in the United Kingdom after William of Orange, leader of the Dutch Republic, occupied the English and Scottish thrones (1689-1702) with his wife Mary.

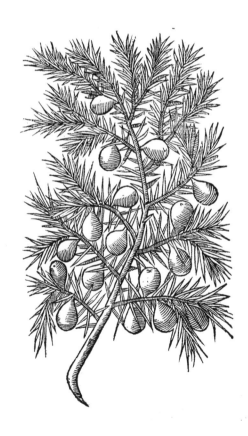

is for *Knautia*
Two brothers they be
Whose dedicated study
Made novel botany

Originally called red scabious or *Scabiosa indica* and *Scabiosa orientalis* it was named *Knautia* by Linnaeus in honour of the brothers Christof and Christian Knaut, physician botanists. Christian developed a pre-Linnaean classification of flowering plants.

is for *Lathryus*
Dig it up with mattocks
Because the seeds ingested
Demolish both one's buttocks

Lathyrus vernus. Spring vetchling, Grass pea, Almorta. The seeds of several *Lathyrus* species are toxic, and when eaten cause aortic aneurysms, spinal cord damage and paraplegia with buttock wasting. This disease is called lathyrism.

Epidemics occur when it is eaten as a 'famine food' when no other food is available.

is for *Lobelia*
For curing you of pox.
Named for a botanist
Who was King James's doc.

Lobelia siphilitica. The genus was named after Matthias de Lobel (1538–1616), Flemish botanist and physician to James I of England, author of the great herbal *Plantarum seu Stirpium Historia* (1576).

This plant was purchased from Native Americans at great cost as it was believed to be their secret cure for syphilis. John Lindley (1838) noted '... European practice does not confirm its American reputation'.

 is for *Mandragora*
A magical thing
Best at a witch's Sabbath
For flying without wings

Mandragora officinare, the mandrake, contains the atropinic alkaloid, hyoscine/scopolamine which paralyses the autonomic nervous system.

This is used as a premedication prior to surgery as it causes sedation and stops vomiting.

In larger doses it causes delirium – in which people (including witches) might get the sensation that they were flying – coma and death.

is for *Matthiolus*
Whose herbals sold so well
Yet cursed his competitors
And wished them all to hell

Matthiola incana, garden Stocks. The genus name commemorates Pietro Andrea Mattioli (1500/1–77), physician, botanist, author and publisher. His commentaries on the *Materia Medica* of Dioscorides were hugely popular, and sold tens of thousands of copies. He was highly antagonistic to any competitors.

'Ten week Stocks' are popular garden annuals, flowering in the year of sowing, whereas 'Brompton Stocks' (another variety of *M. incana*) are biennials, which flower the following year.

is for *Nicotiana*
Death's promises it bears
For all the sad smokers
Of the past five hundred years

Nicotiana tabacum from South America is the tobacco of cigarettes. This is the world's most poisonous plant, killing more people each year than any other. It took over 350 years before this was realised.

Nicotine from the plant is a useful insecticide, but eating it (e.g. boiled leaves) causes vomiting, diarrhoea, slow pulse, respiratory failure and death. It is also teratogenic.

is for *Origanum*
Our Cretan dittany.
The ills that it cures
Make a sweet litany

Origanum dictamnus, Dittany of Crete. Culpeper (1650) writes: ' ... it's an admirable remedy against wounds and Gunshot, wounds made with poisoned weapons, draws out splinters, broken bones, etc.

They say the goats and deer in Crete, being wounded with arrows, eat this herb, which makes the arrows fall out of themselves.'

This magical property was noted by Theophrastus (371-287BC) and in Virgil's *Aeneid* (ca. 15BC).

is for *Olea*
The noble olive tree
Whose bark was used
For curing leprosy

Olea europaea, the olive, was regarded by Dioscorides (70AD) as a panacea, curing all manner of skin diseases from shingles to sores; eye problems to bleeding and for cleaning gums, but the sap he regarded as a deadly poison, an abortifacient, but good for curing leprosy if applied topically.

John Lindley (1838) recommended the bark as a quinine substitute, so it was used for fevers.

Its virtues have gradually descended to becoming an addition to salads.

is for *Paeonia*
Which in the ancient writs
Was hung around a baby's neck
To cure its febrile fits

Paeonia officinalis, the European Peony, commemorates Paeon, physician to the Gods of ancient Greece and father of Aesculapius, the God of medicine.

Galen (200AD) reported that the roots, hung round the neck, were a cure for epilepsy especially in children.

Elizabeth Blackwell's *A Curious Herbal* (1737) explains that this cured febrile fits in children, associated with teething. Although she does not mention it, these stop whatever one does.

is for *Papaver*
Whose sap will set in train
A neurological process
That takes away all pain

Papaver somniferum, the Opium poppy is the oldest medicine in continuous use, described in the Ebers' papyrus (1550BC). Culpeper (1650) writes 'Syrups of Poppies provoke sleep, but in that I desire they may be used with a great deal of caution and wariness ...'.

The alkaloids in the sap include Morphine 12% which causes euphoria, sleepiness, and pain relief; suppresses cough and causes constipation.

is for *Paris quadrifolia*
The leaves a floral love-knot
But poisons cold it does contain
Which quell all passions red-hot

The shape of the four leaves, resembling a Burgundian cross or a true love-knot, caused it to be known as Herb True Love.

The berry is poisonous, so was a 'cold' plant in the Doctrine of the Humours to be used to combat inflammation and hot passions.

It was also used as an antidote to poisoning as the Doctrine of Signatures credited one poison as an antidote to another.

Best regarded as an elegant plant and forget the conflicting properties.

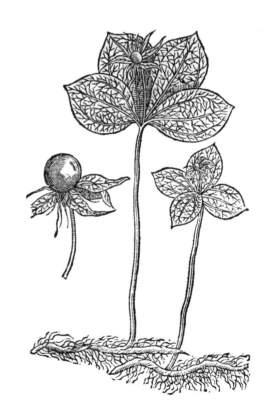

is for *Ricinus*
The source of castor oil
But if you chew the seed coat
You'll end up in the soil

Ricinus communis, the Castor oil plant. The seeds themselves are pretty, brown, bean-like, usually with gold filigree markings on them. The interior of the seed is the source of castor oil, a purgative.

The outer coat of the seed is the source of the poison ricin, famous (infamous) for the umbrella murder of Georgi Markov on Waterloo Bridge in 1978.

is for *Ranunculus*
It always causes smiles
For the knobbly root stock
Was used to cure one's piles

Ranunculus ficaria (now *Ficaria vernus*), Lesser Celandine and Pilewort, has knobbly roots resembling haemorrhoids.

An early English name for haemorrhoid or piles was a 'fig' and 'ficaria' means 'pertaining to piles'. Carrying the roots, or applying a paste made from them, alleviated haemorrhoids/piles, according to Henry Lyte (1578).

is for *Senna*
Which Hippocrates did rumour
Caused depression to be ejected
With the melancholic humour

Senna corymbosa, Senna, is the source of one of the best known of all herbal medicines.

It contains anthraquinones which, when taken internally, act as a powerful laxative to treat constipation, but are dangerous with prolonged use.

Purgation, by ridding the body of the 'black melancholic humour' was a Hippocratic treatment for depression.

is for *Taxus*
And there are few things finer
For tumours, but now as well
It ameliorates angina

Taxus baccata, European Yew.
Its leaves are a source of taxol, an
important treatment for breast and
other cancers.

It works against cancers by stopping
cell division, so is also used in stents
that are inserted to keep coronary
arteries open.

Here it stops the lining cells of the
coronary artery from growing into the
stent and so narrowing it and slowing
blood flow.

is for *Tradescantia*, father and son,
Now long gone
Plantsmen apothecaries
And both called John

Tradescantia was introduced into Britain between 1616 and 1629 by John Tradescant the Elder (d 1638).

He was gardener to King Charles I and travelled, collecting plants in Russia, Algiers and Egypt, maintaining a garden and museum in London. The younger John Tradescant (1608-1662) succeeded his father as the King's gardener, collected mostly in America and brought back 90 new plants.

Their museum is the basis of the Ashmolean in Oxford.

is for *Urtica*
Its stings do not work
If you rub it with *Rumex*
Which nearby does lurk

Urtica dioica, the common stinging nettle causes mildly painful stings from contact with the spiny hairs. The folk-lore treatment for this is to rub the affected part with the leaves of Dock, *Rumex obtusifolius*, which often grows nearby.

The Doctrine of Signatures indicated that the cure for a condition could be found in the same area. For this reason Culpeper averred that English plants should be used for English diseases and that foreign plants could not be expected to work.

is for *Uvularia*
It was used for coughs
By those Americans
Known as Iroquois

Uvularia grandiflora is described in Parkinson's *Theatrum Botanicum* (1640) as '*Polygonatum ramosum flore luteo majus et minus Americanum* ‑ the Greater and Lesse thorow [=through or perfoliate] leaved Solomon's seal of America' and that it had been brought from Canada by the French.

The roots were ground up as a cough mixture by Native Americans.

is for *Valeriana*
Most highly does it rate
As an anti-epileptic
Called sodium valproate

Contains valeric acid, from which valproic acid and then sodium valproate was synthesised.

Sodium valproate is used for epilepsy, neuropathic pain, mania and for migraine prevention. Tragically teratogenic causing foetal abnormalities including autism.

Historically not recorded as a sedative until Martindale in 1936. As a herbal medicine for anxiety it has caused liver failure. Best avoided.

also stands for *Vicia*
Our traditional broad bean
Which helps the Parkinsonian
With extracted dopamine

Vicia faba, the broad bean, is a natural source of L-dopa, a chemical used in the treatment of Parkinson's disease where there is a shortage of dopamine in the brain.

The body converts L-dopa to dopamine which will relieve the symptoms for a variable length of time.

is for *Winteri*
Whose story will relate
That it cured men of scurvy
In 1578

Drimys winteri is named after Captain John Winter who sailed with Sir Francis Drake to raid the Spanish possessions on the Pacific coast of South America.

Parkinson (1640) tells us that in Tierra del Fuego in 1578 Winter's men found that eating the fruits, mixed with honey to make them palatable, cured their scurvy.

Winteranus Cortex, Winter's bark, from the trees became known as a treatment for scurvy.

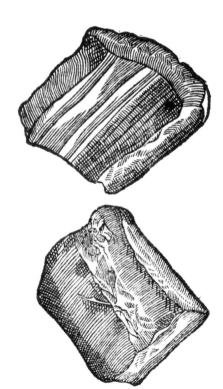

is for *Xyris*
A name for Stinking Gladwin.
And if you strew it on your floors
You will wonder what you stepped in

Xyris, *Spatula foetida*, Stinking Gladwin, Stinking Iris, *Iris foetidissima* has leaves which give off a vile smell when crushed.

The leaves of the tall, yellow-flowered, Flag Iris, *Iris pseudoacorus*, gives off a pleasant fragrance when crushed so was used as a strewing herb, put on the flag stone floors of houses for walking on.

Stinking Gladwin was best avoided for this purpose.

is for *Yucca*
Our presidential knight
Who got the garden started
And made it flourish right

Yucca thompsonii from Mexico is named for Charles Henry Thompson (1870-1930) Assistant Botanist at the Missouri Botanic Garden, in charge of succulents.

Sir Richard Thompson KCVO as Treasurer and President of the Royal College of Physicians of London initiated and supported the new medicinal garden at the College.

While Sir Richard is no relation of the American botanist, this hardy exotic reminds us of his foresight and enthusiasm for the garden.

is for *Ziziphus*
And when the coughing ails us
They used the fruit to accentuate
Syrupus pectoralis

Ziziphus jujuba, the 'Red date' or Jujube. The fruit of this small evergreen tree was used in the manufacture of a superior cough mixture, *Syrupus Jujubinus*, in the 18th century.

This also contained opium, which is a very effective cough suppressant, and lettuce, melon seed, barley, liquorice, violets and maidenhair fern, tragacanth and quinces, with plenty of sugar to hide the taste.

Syrupus pectoralis, a simple cough mixture, only contained maidenhair fern, liquorice and sugar.

Visit
www.oakeleybooks.com
for books by this author